# My Conversations with the Devil at the Crossroads

## AN ODYSSEY OF POEMS AND SHORT STORIES

Sherrie J. Barnes, Esq.

For information regarding special discounts for bulk purchases contact the Publisher:

LaBoo Publishing Enterprise, LLC
staff@laboopublishing.com

Printed and bound in the United States of America

*Special thanks to contributors to this book:*

*Dr. Kathleen Karran-McCoy*

*Derrell Parker, Artwork Page 73*

*Ojwanna Wilson, Art enhancement Page 73*
*Art Images Chapter 4, 5, 6, and 7*

*Dedication:*

*My parents, Gene and Jannie Barnes, the vessels that gave
me life. Jaion Anderson and Delijah Dante Barnes,
the next generation.
R.I.P. Pops.*

*To **EVERYONE** I have encountered on this journey of life.
The good, the bad, and the ugly.
All roads led here.*

"With the stroke of my pen
I can make a churchgoer commit sin
What else can I do, you ask?
I can rewrite the Book of Revelations to come to my end."

Sherrie J. Barnes

# Table of Contents

# Foreword

It was the author Deepak Chopra who said, "Even when you think you have your life all mapped out, things happen that shape your destiny in ways you might never have imagined." Sherrie's life has taken many unplanned turns, especially on November 1, 2007, when the DEA raided her home, arrested her husband, and carted him off to ultimately serve a seventeen-year prison sentence. Nevertheless, this turn launched her into a realm of affective preeminence. In *My Conversation with the Devil at the Crossroads*, she illuminates a ubiquitous level of consciousness in moments when most of us are blinded by the experience itself.

The longer we live, the more we are faced with defining ourselves by ephemeral circumstances and the knock-down, drag-out unpredictability of major life events. Most of us have experienced the pain of betrayal, the love of family and friends, the encroachment of truths we may or may not be ready to deal with or have been too busy to deal with because of life itself. However, Sherrie's skillful management of words engages the reader to connect with pure and raw emotions from cover to cover.

I met Sherrie in college at Florida A&M University. We were teammates on the women's tennis team. We've known each other for over thirty years. In the most defining moments in both our lives, I found Sherrie to embody the virtues Rudyard Kipling expressed in his poem "If" and William Henley's "Invictus." Wise beyond her young years, Sherrie has grown and blossomed with life's peaks and valleys into a beautiful woman and prolific writer who, with the uncomplicated truth, transports you to an *"I know what you mean"* moment with every turn of the page.

When you know Sherrie like I know her, you will understand that each ode is not enlightened conjecture but comes from the core of her modus operandi. She is compassionate, malleable, and firm, all at the same time.

Each of her creative works is enthralling, but one of my favorites, that can only be described as mesmerizing, is the vignette titled, *My Conversation with the Devil at the Crossroads (The Story of the Devil, Mr. Johnson, and Me)*. Every word draws you into the story. You will sense the devil's traps, you will curse the she-devil, you will pray for Sherrie, and you will want Mr. Johnson to say more. You really feel as if you are with Sherrie, walking into hell with her.

Get ready to for your mind to experience an odyssey that will engage, mystify, enlighten, and truly inspire. At the end, you will discover that no matter who you are, the ties that bind us are more common than you think.

Way to go S.B. I am so proud of you!

*Dr. Kathleen Karran-McCoy*

# Introduction

When my manager reviewed this book, she suggested I write a more in-depth introduction of how this book came to being. As I gave it thought, it became clear that there was not just one author, there were two—Sherrie Berry and Sherrie J. Barnes.

Sherrie Berry is my younger self, (pictured at the beginning of Chapter 2 Family and Nostalgia). She saw everything and everybody through her trusted rose-colored glasses. She was vivacious, precocious, fun-loving, trusting, creative, and full of hope. She was very respectful of her elders, and they adored her—from her first-grade teacher, Mrs. Rice, to all her coaches, mentors, parents, grandparents, aunts, uncles, and cousins. Sherrie Berry believed if you were nice to people, they would be nice to you. She saw only the best in people. As she entered her teen years, twenties, and early thirties, Sherrie Berry absolutely believed in the fairy tale of true love, and it showed. When it came to relationships, boyfriends, and marriage, she was as green and dumb as they come lol. She made the worst choices in men and suffered many heartaches and heartbreaks as a result.

Sherrie Berry was also a consummate overachiever. She considered herself a jack-of-all-trades and master of most. Voted Best All-Around in her senior year in high school, Sherrie Berry was indeed confident in her talents. There was not a lot she couldn't do when she put her mind to it. The world was her oyster, and the sky was her limit. She attended college and law school on full scholarships. She was a basketball and tennis standout in high school and lettered in both sports in college. After law school, she went on to become an attorney and started working for the public defender's office. She was known in the office as "trial girl" because she had a great jury trial winning record. After leaving the PD's office, she went on to start her own law practice.

Artistically, Sherrie Berry could make just about anything with her hands. She started off as a child with a love of mixing perfumes with the Fresh and Fancy set she received from her parents as a Christmas gift. As an adult, she made jewelry and her own skin care products. She loved to write poems and short plays. She was hypnotized by nature, imagery, and photography. She loved it all. She did it all.

Sherrie Berry's parents were music lovers. They had a huge collection of records and albums and would play them after work and on Saturday mornings. The 45 RPM record in the background of Sherrie's picture at the beginning of Chapter 2 is of a song she absolutely loved as a child. At the bottom left corner of the record label, there is a big blue and orange bird. The record represents a nostalgic memory that shaped her rose-colored existence. The record, by Erma Franklin (Aretha Franklin's sister), was titled "Piece of My Heart." It turned out to be a classic as it has been covered over seventy times. Erma Franklin's version was the first to be released in 1967. Other notable renditions were by Janis Joplin and Faith Hill. For some reason, three-year-old Sherrie Berry had a special affection for this song, a slow but powerful ballad. Her affinity for it tickled her parents. They thought it was odd but incredibly cute that their three-year-old baby girl would plead, "Play the record with the bird on it." To this day, her pops still has that record, and they still reminisce about the song with the bird . . . and he still plays it for Sherrie Berry.

Sherrie J. Barnes is who Sherrie Berry evolved into after the rose-colored glasses were ripped off and she had to face life without them.

On November 1, 2007, after a series of very bad and misguided decisions—namely entering into a marriage that was doomed from the start—Sherrie Berry's life took a serious turn. On that date, the DEA raided her home and arrested her husband of less than a year. To add insult to injury, the agents that raided her home were some of the same agents she had worked with on previous cases as a federal criminal defense attorney.

I can't divulge what happened that day when the Feds came into Sherrie's home, but the behavior her ex-husband displayed that day and many years after was inconceivable. Sherrie's rose-colored glasses were forcefully ripped from her face and totally shattered.

Enter Sherrie J. Barnes.

Have you ever experienced a shapeshifter? Have you seen someone's face totally change in an instant, and you don't recognize them? Do you ask yourself who this person is because their behavior is so dramatically different from when they initially presented themselves to you? Now don't misunderstand me—I'm not saying my ex-husband hadn't shown some very unfavorable ways in the past. But I'm talking some next-level behavior. I'm talking about the very second a Svengali realizes their gig is up, and they can no longer sucker you because the rose-colored glasses are off. They can't hide their true self—and maybe don't want to. Oftentimes this kind of person secretly resents you because they had to put up a front when around you for so long. Consequently, when they're free from having to pretend they care about you, they shape-shift. Their eyes become black and soulless, and their smiles are crooked. It's like you're looking into the face of evil, of the devil. I experienced this on and after November 1, 2007.

In the months following the raid, it seemed as if all of the shape-shifters came out of the woodwork. All kinds of folks who I thought were in my corner were shapeshifting on a weekly basis. It was like the devil and his army had mounted a full-court press on my life and were trying their best to break me.

It really all started when I met my ex-husband. The relationship was tumultuous to say the least. It was plagued with next-level drama and abuse. I actually thought if my husband experienced someone who really loved him, things would get better. The truth was that I was too proud to admit to everyone that I made a terrible mistake marrying him and knew that the marriage was doomed from the start.

I was an accomplished and well-respected criminal defense attorney with my own law firm. I graduated cum laude from my undergraduate alma mater, received a full scholarship to law school, and passed the Florida bar on my first attempt. I was supposed to be smart. Yet my life was a complete mess. Federal agents had raided my home and arrested my husband for all kinds of criminal charges. He was later sentenced to seventeen years in federal prison, and his businesses went belly up. A couple of years later, I sold my home and walked away from my law practice. And there I was, picking up pieces of my broken existence. Ms. Educated was severely miseducated.

My darkest moment was a terrifying and brutal experience I experienced at the hands of a male colleague I thought was a friend—I'll call him Ted for the purpose of this story. Ted was someone I respected and confided in about the legalities of my ex-husband's case. Someone I entertained the possibility of sharing office space with. Someone I bared my soul to about the despair and anguish I was going through after the Feds raided my home. I knew Ted's family well. He had two daughters, and his wife and I shared the same middle name.

Ted came up from Orlando, Florida one weekend to visit his family in Tallahassee and take a look at my law office to see if it was a space he might want to rent or share. He came to the office on a Friday evening, and as soon as he got in the office and I closed the door, he pounced on me, catching me totally off guard. He started to grope me and tried to kiss me. I was in total disbelief. I told him no, but he proceeded to force himself upon me, and I had to physically fight him off. Let me add that Ted was extremely handsome and fine as hell—he did not have to force anyone to have sex with him.

As I screamed for him to stop, he had a look in his eyes that I had seen before. It was the same soulless, savage look I had witnessed with my ex-husband. Another shape-shifter demon, I thought to myself. And there I was—fighting off a Black Ted Bundy. Ted grabbed me so hard that he bruised my arms and my thighs, and he bit me on the neck as he tried to force me to have sex with him.

The only thing that saved me was the ringing of his cell phone. It was like the sound jerked him out of his sexually-induced attack trance. When he answered the phone, I ran into another area of the office and got my taser and my gun. I pointed the taser at Ted and told him to get the hell out of my office. And he left like nothing had ever happened. No apology. Imagine that.

There I was, a criminal defense attorney whose husband was in federal custody for all kinds of crimes, and I had just been brutally assaulted by a colleague who I thought was a friend—and in my own law office. Needless to say, it was a very sobering experience. I remember sitting on the sofa in my law office with a ripped dress and black and blue bruising, trying to understand what had just transpired. I sat there for what seemed like hours before I called a friend. She came and took pictures of my bruises. She urged me to report him to the authorities, but I wasn't strong enough to deal with this in addition to everything else that was going on. I didn't know where to go, who to trust, and who not to trust. I distinctly remember my friend telling me in the office that night, "It's always darkest before the dawn, Sherrie. This too shall pass." And I remember responding, "It ain't passing quick enough." She chuckled and said, "It will pass on God's time, not yours, chica."

I prayed to God all night long. "Please hurry up and let this pass. I'm not sure how much more I can take." After months of pleading to God to hurry up and let it pass, I stopped asking.

After the incident with Black Ted Bundy, I became very cold and withdrawn. I stayed home a lot and kept the blinds closed. I didn't want to see sunlight. I didn't want to face another day with the present circumstances of my life. When I did manage to muster the strength to get out of bed because of work obligations, it was all I could do to keep up the facade in front of clients and colleagues. As soon as I returned home, I retreated to the sofa or the bed.

While home, I fantasized, plotting revenge on everyone who had betrayed me. The charlatans—my so-called friends, family members, and colleagues who slithered around with fake concern while secretly relishing my dismal circumstances—were all fair game. No one was off-limits. All takers were welcomed. Deep down, I disliked this angry and venomous person I had turned into, but I couldn't go back to the rose-colored glasses. I refused to be anybody's patsy again.

One night, I awoke during the witching hour, and my heart was heavy. The spirit of despair engulfed the air of my entire home. I was so filled with resentment, hurt, and embarrassment. I felt like I was going to choke on the constant replaying in my head of all the horrible experiences I had gone through in the last year. Emotionally and spiritually, I was at rock bottom. I had no idea who I was anymore. The Sherrie Berry that had lived and loved with such hope was gone. I started to ponder many questions . . . What type of person was I? What kind of person had I become? Would I stay bitter and hurt forever? Would I be in guarded revenge mode the rest of my life? And what would I be after "*this too shall pass*"? I was certainly at a crossroads in my life.

All then, all of a sudden, there was a foul and unpleasant odor in the air. I began to cough and couldn't stop. The coughing spell turned into dry heaving. I rushed over to the sink to pour a glass of water. My loyal and beloved Rottweiler, Giant, was right by my side in the kitchen. After a few minutes, the coughing and upchucking subsided, but the odor was still in the air. I burned incense and opened a window then sat on the sofa to rest. Soon, the odor overpowered the smell of the incense, and my coughing and dry heaving started again. I got up for another glass of water—and then it hit me. I realized the spirit of despair in the air in my home was causing my cough and dry heaves, and I knew I had to get out of that house and get some fresh air.

I decided to walk up to the lake in my subdivision with Giant. He was overly protective and guarded me and my home like a soldier. As always, I took my pistol with me when leaving the house. Giant and I started to walk to the lake. The cold winter night air on my face felt good, and I had no coughing or dry heaving once I stepped out that door. When we got to the lake, I sat on a bench and contemplated what had just happened. My only refuge was my home, and it was literally making me sick. What was I going to do? I rested my face in my hands and started to weep. As he did on many a night, Giant lay down next to me on the ground while I cried.

After what seemed like hours, I felt a tap on my shoulder, and Giant started growling. I froze. Who was it? *What* was it? I looked up and saw a figure sitting at the other end of the bench. I couldn't see a face, but I distinctly remember a wide-brimmed black hat and shiny dark blue shoes with shoelaces that glowed. I couldn't get up and leave. I wasn't ready to go back. I couldn't go back to that air of despair that was making me sick. I couldn't continue feeling hurt and angry every day. I was tired of being stuck in the past. But at the same time, I couldn't move forward because I was truly lost with no direction. I didn't know what to do, and I certainly didn't know which way to go. I didn't know who I was anymore. Something *had* to give. I could hear my friend's voice saying, "The only way to get past a situation is to go through it. It's time to put your big girl panties on, chica."

At that very moment, I began to calculate in my head all the night's events and all the extreme hate, hurt, and confusion I was filled with. And I knew it could be only one person sitting at the end of the bench. I calmed Giant down because I knew exactly who it was. I turned toward the devil and said, "I knew you were coming. Just didn't know when."

The devil replied, "I figured now was as good a time as any. Since I'm here, we might as well converse."

So there I was, at the crossroads, face to face with the devil. My very soul was on the line. It was time for me to confront the devil, his demons, and those he assigned to me.

My first conversation was daunting to say the least. It required a deep and deliberate purging. That's why the first chapter of the book is titled

"Self -Reflection." The devil put a mirror to my face and kept it there for a long, long time. I was forced to look at myself. As Michael Jackson said, start with the man in the mirror. I've learned that to evolve on any level, you must first self-analyze. It's not an easy task, and certainly not for the faint of heart.

During the conversation, I had admitted that I had made a lot of selfish decisions. I also had to come clean and admit that I was very good at analyzing and finding fault in others. I considered myself to be a giving and compassionate person that never set out to use or hurt people. However, the mirror the devil kept to my face forced me to see times when I didn't consider others' feelings because I was too consumed with my own. The floodgates of guilt, sorrow, and shame opened up in my soul, and I had to take a long hard look at myself.

Self-reflection is a necessary—and dark—time. It requires you to recollect your poor actions in the past and face the secrets you have hidden—secrets that if people knew, they might judge you harshly for. Self-reflection breaks you down—the secrets you've buried start to haunt you in your dreams and dominate your thoughts. Taking a long look in that mirror is cathartic because it forces you to see that you have no pedestal and no right to stand in judgment of anyone or anything. When you think about finding fault in others, ask yourself, "What if people knew my secrets? What if my past misdeeds were discovered and became public?"

The first conversation with the devil took its toll on me. Good thing I've always been a competitor because I was compelled to go back. I was still at a major crossroads in life, and the devil and I had unfinished business. For the next few months, I walked to the lake with Giant once a week around the witching hour. And on cue, the devil would show up within a few minutes of our arrival.

One of the most fascinating tricks the devil pulled during our conversations was appearing in a different physical form each time. Sometimes it would be someone from my past—an old teacher, an old coach, a family member, a past lover, or someone I didn't remember at all. One time, it was Old Saint Nick. Imagine that! Each time, we conversed about a different topic, each represented by a chapter in the book. The morning after my conversation with the devil, I could never remember what we discussed the night before—with one exception. I remembered the conversation about self-reflection. I will never forget that mirror.

Spring was coming. I got up one night and walked to the lake with Giant. I remember the exact date—March 24. This night was different. The moon was extremely bright and hanging low. Its reflection on the lake was stunning. The stars were plentiful as well. They were bright, and I swear they were twinkling. Giant and I sat on the bench and waited for over an hour, but the devil never showed. Giant did something different that night. Instead of lying on the ground next to my feet, he jumped up onto the bench and sat next to me. I smiled because I knew that meant the devil wasn't coming back anytime soon. As Giant and I got up to walk back home, I heard a guitar strumming a lil diddley. I slept so soundly that night.

The next morning, I awoke on the sofa. The blinds were closed, but a ray of light had forced its way through them and reflected off the back of a CD on the floor, creating a magnificent rainbow against my wall. Every color was so vivid and clear, and it was one of the most breathtaking sights I had ever seen. Just like the big, bright, low-hanging moon reflecting off the lake the night before. An immediate awakening rose up in me. I saw that beautiful rainbow as a sign from the Creator that everything was going to be all right, and my pot of gold was on the way. I immediately got up, cleaned up the house, and started to write.

I've been an artist and a writer of short stories and poems since I was a child, but this experience was much different—it was divinely magical. As I began to write, my words flowed as powerfully and consistently as the majestic Horseshoe Falls in Niagara Falls, Canada. It was like a portal in my soul opened up and poured everything I had experienced in my entire life into my written words. There was no writer's block. I didn't have to think about the words—they wrote themselves. I was in a trance, and my pen moved in sync with my soul. I time-traveled back to the experiences I was writing about. My creativity was at its apex. I had literally ascended into the fifth dimension, and for the next few weeks, I lived in that dimension. Everything was inspiration for a poem or short story—family, nostalgic memories, politics, a conversation, music, traveling, forgiveness, flowers on the side of the road, meeting new people, history, love, tennis, pain, gratitude, romance, laughter, confusion, pride, death, fear. Everything!

The journey from Sherrie Berry to Sherrie J. Barnes and the hereinafter is my collection of poetry and short stories that detail my conversations with the devil at the crossroads.

I hope this book touches your soul deep, deep down. The journey begins . . .

# Part 1

## Chapter 1

# Self-Reflection

*"House of a thousand lies, journey of a thousand goodbyes,
tears of a thousand cries, land where a thousand dies.
Flesh of my flesh, bone of my bone,
seems like he who is full of sin
**always** casts the first stone."*
**Sherrie J. Barnes**


*"Not everything that is faced can be changed,
but nothing can be changed until it is faced."*
**James Baldwin**

# Secrets

Secrets, secrets, we all have secrets
*Some, we should never tell.*
*Secrets, secrets, we all have secrets*
*That detain us in living hells.*

*Do you ever really know someone?*
*Does someone ever really know you?*
*Ghosts of our past on nightly watch*
*To haunt the essence of what is true.*

*When we look into a mirror*
*Who do we really see?*
*Not a face of pure honesty*
*Nor a person secret-free.*

*Secrets, secrets, tell me your secrets*
*The ones that only walls know*
*And I'll show you a view into a disrobed soul*
*That must reap his secret's sow.*

*When someone tells you they have no secrets*
*It's an untruth you cannot believe*
*Just turn it around and ask yourself,*
*"How many times have I deceived?"*

*Was it a small indiscretion?*
*Or the proverbial white lie?*
*Was it an omission of the truth?*
*Or did you break the binds that tie?*

*Secrets, secrets, we all have secrets*
*When exposed the price can be steep.*
*How many secrets have you revealed?*
*What kind of secrets do you keep?*
*Shhhhhhhhhh . . .*

# I Broke **All Ten** Commandments

I broke all Ten Commandments
If there were sixteen, they would be broken too
The nature of the beast stalks all of us
To do whatever we want to do

Now don't let me get off track
This is the story of me
The good, the bad, the ugly
The complication of my dichotomy

Call me a home-wrecker
A Jezebel without a doubt
A veteran of sinful pleasures
I've traveled miles of detoured route

Tasted forbidden paradise
More than any good girl should
Gratified by my vices
Simply because I could

I've lied—does that make me a liar?
I've cheated—am I a cheat?
I have fornicated and I have stolen
I have been a sore loser in defeat

Consumption was in my blood
Indulged too many times to name
The dreams I have to remember
I had to numb and mask the pain

I have despised my next-door neighbor
Lilith, the mold I readily broke
Cursed in a matrix of selfishness
Stayed in conditions absent of hope

Did I mention destruction and carnage?
I'm guilty of that too
No gun, no sword, no poison
Just no guts to see it through
The story of me is a valuable lesson
Never umpire my fellow man
See him as only human
No pedestals can I stand.

# The Hater's Prayer

Now I lay me down to sleep
I pray to God my soul to keep
If I don't die before I wake
Please reveal those around me who are fake
The ones who manipulate and perpetrate
That if I turned my back, they'd plant a stake
As I lay tonight in my bed
Please delete the demons from my head
The misery, the confusion, especially the dread
Redirect my path where I've been misled

Lord, please let the haters make me greater
As I travel among the movers and the shakers
Let me stand up and speak for myself like a great debater
And bow down only to my maker
Don't let me be taken by the takers
Unveil the treachery of all the forsakers

Let love and peace be my top mission
May I pick and choose my battles with sharp precision
When in doubt rear me to the right decision
Let the virtue of my patience come to fruition

In the morning when I rise
Please keep my eyes on the prize
As I soar high with eagles in blue skies
Far from the crabs that plot my demise

Break me away from all negative ties
Help me detect all bad vibes
Make me allergic to untruths and lies
And uncover the mask of a hater's disguise

All day may my thoughts be pure
Let me be courageous and not unsure
Make certain any troubles I will endure
To shake the haters off, this prayer is my cure

And for all my true blue friends
Please keep our friendships on the mend
To their *own* business let the haters tend
These and other blessings I ask ... AMEN

# Chapter 2
# Family & Nostalgia

*Back Down Melody Lane*

*"Ain't nothing like my family,*
*when the world has taken its toll.*
*Going home to real love, refueling an empty soul."*
**Sherrie J. Barnes**

# Granny's Front Porch
(Passing of the Torch)

Lately, I've been thinking about
The passing of the torch
Four generations of family
Sitting on my granny's front porch

Let me tell you about Granny's porch
A place where kinfolk secrets were revealed
Gossip told and wisdom passed down
Family wounds forgiven and healed

Granny's porch was very special
All day people walked by
Babies were born and children grew up
Loved ones passed on to the other side

Over the years on Granny's porch
The world made significant change
Family dynamics altered
And completely rearranged

However, my family stayed true
Despite struggle, aggravation, and inflation
I marvel at how they made it
Through all kinds of situations

I thank them for their love
Loyalty and dedication
Each one teach one was their philosophy
They laid the groundwork for the next generation

Home ownership, entrepreneurship, education
An appreciation of nature and the land
A legacy of giving, hard work, and respect
Long before Barack said, "Yes we can."

When I braid my auntie's hair
And me and Momma at the table playing cards
My uncles revisiting the "good old days" again and again
All of them tired from years of working so hard

Watching Daddy Pops tend his garden
In his prized two-acre backyard
I know I must step up
It's time for a changing of the guards.

# The Simple Things

Fireflies in flight
Ignite dusky skies with flashing lights
Brings back childhood memories of summer nights
Oh, how I long for the simple things in life

Sticky, sticky candy fingers
When a Band-Aid covered a hurt
Running down the ice cream man
Momma waking you up to go to church

Walking home from school
A double-dog dare
Like a belly flop into a swimming pool
Or winning a prize at the fall fair

The sound of a vinyl record
Homemade biscuits, fish and grits
Riding on bicycle handlebars
The simple things, I really miss

Roller skating and playing jacks
Watching a soaring kite
Quenching your thirst from a water hose
Grandmomma rubbing alcohol on mosquito bites

Watching early morning cartoons
Richard Pryor in *Uptown Saturday Night*
When all your loved ones were alive and well
Oh, how I long for the simple things in life

# Ain't Nothing Like My Family

Ain't nothing like my family
when the world has taken its toll
Going home to real love
refueling an empty soul

Nothing like gossiping aunties
That always put on a pot for you
Collard greens, turkey wings, and biscuits
A loving open door policy too
Nothing like jousting with Stokely
While Ms. Spelman makes us brunch
Give back, rise above, and strive harder
Is his food for thought to munch

Nothing like laughing with Momma
Reminiscing on times, truth, and lies
Chuckling at present-day drama
To ease the pain of loved ones gone by

Hanging out with my cousins
Doing what we like to do
Riding through the neighborhood with my sisters
Sipping on Woodchuck Brew

Card-playing is a ritual
Spades all night on the Ave
Smokers vs. the Big Butts
Nothing but a good time to have!

Nothing like growing up with love
Family fights and fallouts
Waking to the smell of breakfast
Brings comfort among many doubts

Ain't nothing like corner store scratch-offs
And my lil sister's aggravation
Nothing like Auntie across the street
And her regaling stories of sensation

Ain't nothing like picking from the garden
Blessed with serendipity
Can't choose your kin folks
But ain't nothing like *my* family

# Oooooooh, Take Me Back, Take Me Back

Oooooooh, take me back, take me back . . .
Walking to the corner store
hearing the sounds of Planet Rock
Booming with bass in the "Atl,"
at the Edward J. Shop

When the daily menu was Doritos, Lemonheads,
and the biggest pickle in the jar
Pixie Stixs, Peach Nehi, and a king-size candy bar

Getting high meant the score on Ms. Pacman,
Galaga, Donkey Kong, and Centipede
When it was embarrassing at school to never have the lead

When everyone you loved was alive and well
And you pinky swore to keep a secret and never ever tell

Playing outside all day, not caring how you looked
Carrying lunch boxes to school, brown paper bags covered your schoolbooks

When you got into trouble at the house of a friend
Then came home and got beat all over again

When class field trips were as revered as spring break
When you hadn't discovered that people could be *so fake*
**Ooooooooohhhh, take me back, take me back . . .**

Back down melody lane
Love, Peace, and SOOOOOUUUUL Train
Catching lightning bugs in your hands, and dancing in the rain

When a snowy day was the ultimate dream come true
On the last day of school you saw a fistfight or two

When TV would go off after the Star-Spangled Banner
When kids had respect for their elders *and* good manners

Riding the waterlogs at Six Flags,
making up games for kicks
Brain freeze from a Popsicle,
and a thirst only the ice cream man could fix

When getting faster at "tweet a leet"
was the most important thing to learn
Hopscotch on the sidewalk
made the bottoms of your Chuck Taylor's burn

When sock hops and dances
were as anticipated as Christmas Eve
When a Black doll was hard to find,
and a bad world you couldn't conceive
**Ooooooooh, please take me back, take me back . . .**

When your biggest fear was a parent with a belt
And you ate sandwiches with "government" cheese
that just wouldn't melt.

Girls wore cornrows with a thousand beads in their head
When you thought the boogeyman
was hiding under your bed

When "Who shot JR?" was a major contemplation
*Good Times*, *The Six Million Dollar Man*, and *Fantasy Island*
were the topics of conversation

Visiting your grandma in the summer for a few weeks
And she told you to *hush* during a thunderstorm
because it was God's turn to speak

Slapping five on the Black Hand side
and picking out your afro
Hoping to get a glimpse of the tooth fairy
and find the end of a rainbow.

When your biggest disappointment
was being picked last for a team
When things in your life
*were* as good as they seemed
**Ooooooooh, take me back, take me back** . . .

# Chapter 3
# The "Cotton Pickin'" Truth

*Cotton Fields, Marianna, Florida*
*Photo by Sherrie J. Barnes*

"*Do you know how close Marshall Law is to being instituted?*
*Do you know the extent that our earth is polluted?*
*The MAN's Plan is to keep your mind diluted*
*If I'm lying, somebody dispute it.*"
**Sherrie J. Barnes**


"*Toto, I don't think we are in Decatur anymore.*"
**Sherrie J. Barnes**

# If I Was a Politician?

If I was a politician, who would I be?
Not many left to choose from
With any integrity
False campaign promises
Involvement in illegal activity
On a scale of one to ten
They score a zero on credibility

Back-door deals, secret agendas,
Bi-partisan hypocrisy
With all this corruption in government
How can they make laws to govern me?

Both Republicans and Democrats
Inducted into the political hall of shame
The list goes on and on and on
I just don't know all of their names

Is there a method to their madness?
Will their behavior ever come to a halt?
If I was a politician, who would I be?
The politician that couldn't be bought

# My Christmas List

When I wake on December 25
And look under my Christmas tree
I hope there's a *big, big* present
Especially just for me

I want a billion-dollar bailout
Like the Federal Reserve gave AIG
And let me unwrap a world filled with peace
As far as every eye can see

Please stuff my Christmas stocking
With a little Patron on the rocks
I would also *love to* have
A turn-back on the hands-of-time clock
So I can sit with Otis Redding
As he serenades me on the dock
And watch MJ moonwalk again
You know, the undisputed King of Pop
And please give me the top
To put back on Pandora's Box
Let the prize patrol be at my door
The next time I hear a knock

However, there is *one more thing*
I sincerely ask for
That folks don't tell their kids
About no Santa Claus anymore

'Cause ain't no imaginary man
Anywhere around I know
Gonna travel in one night with reindeer
In a bunch of snow

To bring kids all over the world
Gifts, games, and toys
Especially not fast little girls
Or bad-behind little boys

Tell your kids the truth
If you don't know what to say
Santa Claus are the parents and grown-ups
Working hard everyday

And certainly not some imaginary hope
I wanna kill the myth of Santa Claus
 Give me a noose made out of rope

Then I'm gonna use that rope
To hang the myth of Santa
as an ornament on my Christmas tree
As a reminder that ain't no imaginary man
Gonna give me nothing for free

OMG! I killed Santa
So who's gonna bring me the things I wish?
Guess I'll call my boyfriend up
And give him my Christmas list

# The MAN's Plan

*Hear Ye, Hear Ye!*
I am about to take a stand
The Kingdom of Heaven is at hand
Let me kick to you all the knowledge that I can
And give you thoughts to ponder regarding The MAN's Plan

Will Black folks ever totally be free?
Will the government ever admit their hypocrisy?
Will people stop believing all that propaganda on TV?
Do we coexist with life outside our galaxy?

Did you know the ingredients in your diet drink
are the same found in rat poisons
sitting under your kitchen sink?
You better get away from everybody and seriously think
The world as we know it may soon be extinct

For this next verse, you may need some liquor libations
The MAN's Plan is to fill your head with sports and entertainment sensation
Keep you bogged down with bills and inflation
So you don't focus on the real situation

Do you know how close Marshall Law is to being instituted?
Do you know the extent that our earth is polluted?

The MAN's Plan is to keep your mind diluted
If I'm lying, somebody dispute it

The FDA tells you foods and prescription drugs are safe
But the numbers of recalls and chemicals in them are great
Irrespective of their expiration date
Why do you think cancer is at an alarming rate?
This point can you dispute or debate?
If you do not take the time to educate?

The Law persecuted number seven
And took him out of the game
When there's a TV channel
dedicated to killing animals for sport
Isn't that the same thang?

What about the TV shows?
Where humans fight inside a cage
Beating each other unconscious
Now, I am outraged!

What is *the difference*, I ask?
I guess it's *all about getting paid*
It never ever ceases to amaze me
How people pick and choose their crusades

In closing, let me make a few more things clear
Always question anything you hear
Take time to learn and not to fear
Thank you very much for lending your ear
**Power to the People!**

# Flee the Sweet Land of Bigotry

What was that song I hear?
Peg Leg Joe singing sounds so sweet
Telling me in cryptic code
When it's time to move my feet

Through the woods and cross the river
Past the Mason-Dixon Line
For this one chance at freedom
I won't be left behind

If I get thirsty on the trip
I be drinking from the gourd
Sharing with everybody
'Til we all on one accord

Is that Black Moses I see up yonder?
That's the baddest woman around
Say she never lost a passenger
On dat railroad underground

Moses say, when a White person pass us by
And we see him touch his ear
Follow him close behind
To a safe house in the clear

Showed us some other signs
Like the secret handshake
Messages sewed on quilts
Lanterns burning after daybreak

Can't stop just up north
Still got a bounty on my head
If massa and his crew catch me
I be whipped, or I be dead

My country 'tis of thee
Sweet land of bigotry
To be free, I flee
A confederate hypocrisy

Cross the border to Canada
Where I have a right to vote
I can own my own land
 . . . Gotta catch that last boat.

# Chapter 4
# Broken and Other Matters of the Heart

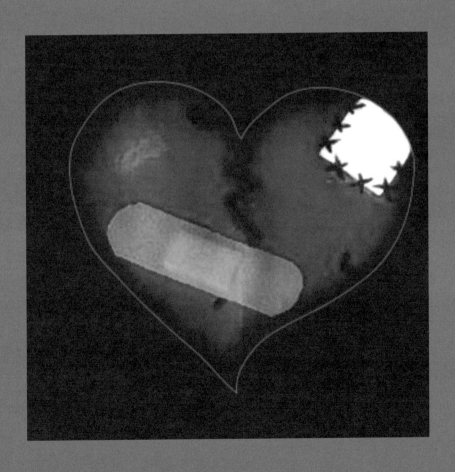

*"Is this the part you take my heart to wipe your feet on?"*
**Loose Ends**


*"Besieged by the death of many loved ones,*
*that I still deeply mourn.*
*I prayed for serenity, I prayed for calm,*
*like the kind before the storm."*
**Sherrie J. Barnes**

# Chivalry Ain't Dead

Escorted me down the plank walk
*To drown in your polluted abyss*
*A cancer with no chemo*
*Death was in your kiss*

*Opened the car door of mistrust*
*Took me on a real, real long ride*
*Helped me with my seatbelt*
*As I rode shotgun in your lies*

*Held my hand so gently*
*Strolling me on the path of no esteem*
*Politely asked my ambitions*
*As you conspired to destroy my dreams*

*Paid the check at dinner*
*Wined and dined all my insecurities*
*Whispered sweet nothings in my ear*
*Only to magnify my impurities*

*Laid a coat over a puddle of water*
*So I could step over your real self*
*Placed me in deliberate peril*
*Then pretended to be the help*

*Walked me to my front door*
*What a gentleman—or so I thought*
*Chivalry . . . it ain't dead*
*A lesson I have painfully been taught.*

# Joy and Pain

Life is full of joy and pain
*That's what the old folks say*
*I pondered that sentiment for a while*
*As I sat around thinking the other day*

*I've had my share of both*
*Mostly all at the same time*
*A litany of bittersweet moments*
*Are etched forever in my mind*

*Where there was hope, there was disappointment*
*Where there was birth, there was death*
*Where there was triumph, there was tragedy*
*The price for every precious breath*

*I've experienced the good and the bad*
*Endured for better or for worse*
*Had a heap of mixed blessings*
*Received the gift and the curse*

*As I sat around thinking the other day*
*I wondered if life's seesaw would ever, ever end?*
*Then I realized pain was necessary*
*For joy to come again*

# Miss-Educated on Love

I was Miss-Educated on love
And the proverbial wish
To find all that's good and kind
Someone to love, someone to miss

I was Miss-Educated on love
Compromised principle and pride
Jailed by your bottomless needs
Integrity laid to the side

I was Miss-Educated on love
And your existence of calamity
Thrived in baby momma drama
Never-ending chaos with family

I was Miss-Educated on love
Turned a blind eye to disrespect
Desensitized to mistreatment
An albatross around my neck

I was Miss-Educated on love
Cursed when I entered your world
Scarred by your endless insecurities
Possessed by the naivety of a girl

*I was Miss-Educated on love*
*Until the day reality bit*
*Delusions completely exposed*
*Damn, I was in some shit*

*I was Miss-Educated on love*
*Divisive moments of contemplation*
*Your mission: seek and destroy*
*Your weapon: manipulation*

*I was Miss-Educated on love*
*All messed up inside my dome*
*Poisoned by your toxic touch*
*A victim of Stockholm syndrome*

*I must be Miss Re-Educated on love*
*Now that I am released from your decay*
*Bled 'til your venom dissipated*
*Rome was certainly not built in a day*

# Tribute to "Coach"

This is not goodbye
It is merely a *so long*
You left a lasting legacy
For us to carry on

Always a kind word
And a heart of pure gold
A pioneer and a mentor
You poured tennis into so many souls

And if anyone has something bad
To say when it comes to you
I'll remind them very quickly
They are imperfect too

When I start to feel sad
And need a little lift
I'll think of how you made everyone feel special
It was God's greatest gift

I will sleep good tonight
Knowing you are in good company
With your mother, Coach Mungen,
And the rest of your family

So this is not goodbye
We will see each other again
You will always be so dear to me
My Coach, my brother, my friend

*In loving memory of Norman Wilkerson "Coach"*
*March 11, 1963 – July 5, 2008*

# Chapter 5
# Smelling the Roses

*"Count your blessings, cut your losses,
and follow the yellow brick road."*
**The Wiz (The Movie)**


*"Thankful to be alive and healthy.
A task most find too remiss.
Taking the time to give back . . .
Heaven must be like this."*
**Sherrie J. Barnes**

# Spring

Butterflies emerge and come out to play
Pollen awakes and brings the fever of hay

Bumble bees buzz, having much to say
Sunshine and blue skies rest above all day

Not too hot and not too cold
Mother Nature brags as her magnificence unfolds

April showers renew and May flowers explode
Blooming with colors so vibrant and bold

A new attitude, a new motivation
The season to awe all of Earth's creations

Just being outside is the *best* seat in town
I feel alive when Spring comes around!

# ... Heaven Must be Like This

Feeling true love
Sweet as a lover's kiss
Eyes meeting in destiny . . .
*Heaven must be like this*

A moonlight stroll
The smallest pleasures we miss
Like the caress of a hand . . .
*Heaven must be like this*

Living life with dreams
A day filled with wedded bliss
Living with no regrets . . .
*Heaven must be like this*

The sound of playing a vinyl record
A great set of tennis
The smell of a summer barbecue . . .
*Heaven must be like this*

Taking the road less traveled
The power of forgiveness
A warm and tender hug . . .
*Heaven must be like this*

Thankful to be alive and healthy
A task most find remiss
Taking time to give back . . .
*Heaven must be like this*

A baby in your arms
An adolescent's appreciativeness
Learning from the wise . . .
*Heaven must be like this*

Having a true friend
In times of loneliness
Laughter through pain . . .
*Heaven must be like this*

Nostalgic memories from the past
A family gathering playing bid whist
Feet under Momma's table . . .
*Heaven must be like this*

Acceptance of change
A spirit of true humbleness
Loving yourself as you are . . .
*Heaven must be like this.*

# Tea with Athena

One enchanting afternoon,
*The goddess Athena and I had tea*
*She told me the angels were up all night*
*Creating a masterpiece*

*I inquired as to its whereabouts*
*And wondered what could it be*
*Athena told me to turn around and look*
*I saw a breathtaking tapestry*

*Gorgeous hues of the horizon*
*Unknown treasures of the deep sea*
*Patterns of sparkling crystals*
*Representing life and its mysteries*

*Silky spools of joy and pain*
*Intertwined threads of dichotomy*
*Pearls of wisdom from experience*
*Roots from a decided family tree*

*I asked her over and over,*
*"Have you ever seen such artistry?"*
*Athena politely smiled*
*and took a sip of her sun-kissed tea*

*She told me to turn around again and look*
*It was a mirror, and in the reflection was me*
*Athena then whispered in my ear,*
*"Now you are free, because you see*
*Beauty in the darkest valley*
*and on top of the highest peak."*

*Grateful, awed, and amazed*
*At the next words she chose to speak,*
*"You saw your reflection this time, dear heart,*
*Because YOU are the masterpiece."*

# Chapter 6
# Pot Luck
*(An odyssey of short stories)*

*"Life is Like a box of Sherries…*
*You never know who you are going to get."*
**Sherrie J. Barnes**


*"Don't know what I mean?*
*Then please continue to read.*
*Follow the lesson carefully, as I take the lead."*
**Sherrie J. Barnes.**

# Adam and Eve, and Lilith
## *"A Love Triangle"*

## ACT I
# The Genesis

In the beginning, it was me, *The Original Woman.* My name is Lilith. I was Adam's *first* wife. See, Eve was just sloppy seconds, created after I refused to submit to Adam's might.

When God made us,
Adam and I came from the same dust.
We were created equal. Eve came from Adam's rib. So she was my submissive sequel.

When Adam was mine, he wanted to be on top *all* the time. I got bored, so lovemaking came to a halt. Adam was furious with me and screamed, "I'm unhappy, Lilith, and it's all your fault!" Like cats and dogs, we fought continuously. He just couldn't appreciate my power of thought.

Adam was not pleased at all…
I could see it all over his face. That's when I knew in the Garden of Eden, for me, there was no place.

So instead, I fled,
And as I waved goodbye, Adam said, "Lilith, don't go. I promise to clean up my act. I'll send angels after you, baby. Anything to get you back!"

As I tried to run and flee to the edge of the Red Sea, I noticed three of the prettiest angels following behind me, as pure as they could be.
I stopped and listened to their plea.

Angel 1 said, "Girl, you better go home and get your man." Angel 2 mumbled, "If she doesn't, *hmmp*... I understand." Angel 3 demanded, "Lilith, you better stop trying to be so grand."
Angel 1 pleaded, "Work it out with Adam if you can."

I told the angels, "Listen, I know if I return, it would eventually be all on Adam's terms. This is a valuable lesson my husband just has to learn. My love and respect, he must cherish and earn."

After the angels continued to school me
on all the do's and don'ts, they finally asked, "Lilith, what do you really want?"
I sighed as I replied, "I want our spirits to coexist in the boondocks of the Milky Way,
where our love is a constant rebirth—
He, my Supernova, and I, his Nebula.
And we have a child and call her *the Universe*."

Angel 1 exclaimed," That is *so beautiful,* girl!"

Angel 2 sobbed, "It brought tears to my eyes."

Angel 3 reasoned, "For the chance of love like that, girl, maybe you should go back."

Angel 2 added, "Before saying any final goodbyes."

Angel 1 confided, "Adam is miserable without you.

He cries out day and night. If you come back, he promises that he will not fuss and fight."

# ACT II
# The Return to the Garden of Eden

Well, Adam cried a very short song. When I returned to the Garden of Eden, Eve had come along.

I must admit, I thought I would be Adam's only wife—until he completely wrote me out of his life. Because the last time I looked, the name "Lilith" is not mentioned in Chapter 1 of the Good Book.

However, "Lilith" is mentioned in the Book of Isaiah as a horrific and demonic winged beast

that devours 100 newborn babies,

as the curse of my daily feast.

"I am so disgusted. Damn it, Adam, it was you I trusted! Now this is too much for any woman to handle. Bossed around, replaced, discarded, and disgraced. Tossed aside as a mythical Bible scandal. Nah, I'm not going to take this lying down. My heart you have ripped and torn. If you want scandal, I will give you plenty. Hell hath no fury like a woman scorned."

"My dear Adam, since you have denied me with such insistence,

I have few questions about you and Ms. Eve being the first in existence.

If Adam and Eve were the first people on earth, and you all had two sons, answer this question for me, where did Cain and Abel's wives come from?

By themselves, men cannot procreate, so how did the bloodline continue to flow?

Now that's a real Bible scandal to ask the preacher man about.

Tell him inquiring minds want to know."

# FINAL ACT
# Eve and Lilith (The Confrontation)

"Here we are finally face to face, me and the woman that took my place. So, you are this chick named Eve. I see through all your mascara and that phony weave. You married my Adam without a divorce. Yet you show no shame, absolutely no remorse."

Eve scowled, "Back off, girly. Adam made his choice! I get him to do whatever I want with my charm,
not by force."
Then she turned and kissed Adam, oh so sweet and passionately, as the serpent handed her a shiny red apple
from the forbidden knowledge tree.

Eve placed the apple to Adam's mouth. It was like he was spellbound and hypnotized. She told him to bite, and with all his might, Adam obediently complied.

I knew I had just witnessed the fate of sin cast on every human soul. The gravity of this very moment was equivalent to—more than—all the lies that have ever been told.

I angrily asked, "Of all the things you could have coerced Adam to do, why would you play with his mind and convince him to eat that serpent's apple, destroying the future of all mankind?"

Eve cavalierly answered, "I could shoot you a bunch of bull and tell you we were so in love. But the truth is I was sick of Adam bossing me around, so I put my iron fist in a velvet glove.
In the Garden of Eden
I could never relax. Adam demanding,
'Eve cook this. Eve go get that.'
He was constantly telling me what to do, and whined like a little baby if I didn't want to.
So I decided it was time to even the score. The art of seduction is the tactic I began to implore.
I tempted Adam to cross his own Creator. What betrayal do you know of that could be any greater?
Tunnel vision is what Adam chose to see. He was intimidated by you when he really should've been afraid of me."

Eve continued to explain,
"See, Lilith, your power of thought was overt. Like most men, Adam couldn't handle that. So I hid my disguise with fake charm and lies, and clouded him with a plethora of sexual attacks.
I made him feel like he was *The Mac*. I gave him the kind of satisfaction that brought the curious cat back!"

I chuckled to myself. Ms. Eve was not submissive at all. Poor Adam never stood a chance in her kind of corruption. He thought the grass was greener—and that I was meaner. And he traded Lilith in . . . for the *Eve of Destruction*.

# Passing the Florida Bar

In 1998, April 15 is the precise date
Destiny appeared, and rendered my fate

See, on that very day
I was sworn into the Florida bar
As a licensed attorney
After a law school career that was extremely subpar

And although I did not graduate high in my class
The first time I took the bar, I was determined to pass

To celebrate graduation
A trip to the casino in Biloxi, Mississippi I took
Went a few more times after that
On the road studying my bar exam books

But my first trip was special
Because an angel rode with me
She revealed the exact bar exam subjects
to focus on and study

The angel was my friend's grandmother
Who had attended our law school graduation
My friend was driving her grandmother back home to Alabama. She
told me it may be a difficult situation.
She explained, "My grandma has Alzheimer's,
so sometimes she does not know what's going on.
If you can bear with it,
we can stop at the casino in Biloxi on the way back.
And generally, girl, nothing goes wrong."

I eagerly agreed to go
for two very different reasons
My beloved granny was still living
And she was in life's winter season

See, grandmothers are precious to me
Treasures that can never be replaced
I had wonderful grandmothers
Memories of them I will never erase

Now, my second reason for going
Was to hit the casino
I received lots of money for graduation
So I had a few dollars to blow

However, Grandma did have a dementia episode
It was heart-wrenching to see
At times Grandma couldn't remember either of us
She kept screaming, "Who are you? Who is she?"

My goodness, Grandma seemed so frightened
Through my friend's patient instructions, I was enlightened

The situation was soon diffused
And thankfully, Grandma was no longer confused

We arrived and dropped Grandma off in Alabama
With family and she finally got settled
Then we headed to the casino
My friend put the pedal to the metal

Thoughts of quick riches danced in my brain
As we traveled east on Interstate 10
Couldn't wait to see and hear the lights, bells, and whistles
Hoping a jackpot one of us would win

Well, neither of us hit the jackpot
But we had a really good time
I hit triple sevens on a few occasions
But I was only playing quarters and dimes

So we headed back home to study
And returned to our daily lives
She dropped me off at my apartment
And then we said our goodbyes

My friend called me a couple of days later
Said her Grandma asked about me
She thought I was a nice, sweet girl
I was surprised she even remembered me

Grandma told her she had a dream
And received a message from angels in heaven
See, out of seventeen bar exam subjects
Randomly, we were only tested on eleven

Grandma revealed the subjects the angels informed her
Would specifically be on the test
I believed everything Grandma said
Now it was up to me for the rest

As I sat for the bar exam
I realized Grandma's dream was right
I answered every question she predicted
I slept so well that night

A couple of months later
My passing results came in
I was a member of the Florida bar
Thanks to Grandma and my friend

# My Conversation with the Devil at the Crossroads

(The Story of the Devil, Mr. Johnson, and Me)

I met the devil today at the infamous crossroads
She asked me to sit down and take off a load
Showed me a vision that I must unfold
Tried to convince me to sell my only soul.

She showed me the friends I knew back when
Who sold me out for a few dollars
You know that ain't right, made me toss and turn at night
Like Marvin Gaye, it made me wanna holla!

I knew I was about to have a melee with a real live beast
In my defense, a tongue lashing I decided to unleash
I started to feel my anger steadily increase
Smelling my hateful spirit, the devil was eager to feast
Now, pay close attention
Because this story is about to get real deep
The devil's evil deeds—on it, I must speak

I told her about the folks who had plotted my demise
her Satan-sent army I really do despise
The constant betrayals caused me many, many cries
So much manipulation, a plethora of lies
My heart was broken and wounded
and my spirit needed to revive
It took me quite a while to finally get wise.

The devil asked a question and wanted me to agree,
"If you are so wise, Sherrie, why are you sitting here with me?"
Then she said, so cold and cavalierly,
"My army almost brought you down is what I see
because you are so far from all you can be,
and thank you for letting me control *your* destiny."
She said it with such venom and so wickedly
And then rolled her evil eyes as she laughed at me

When the she-devil saw
that I was heated and steamed,
she cooed, "Getting in your head is easy.
Look at you—see what I mean?
Here with me at the crossroads
instead of busy pursuing your dreams.
Filling your head with misery and dread,
is all part of my master scheme."

When I realized I was so close to selling my soul
I knew it was time to see just what my fate would hold
So I decided to take a long look
down the she-devil's hellish road
And the things I saw there made my blood run cold.

I saw the people who kill and rape, the ones full of hate,
the liars and the cheats, the cowards and the sneaks
I met the fakers and the haters,
the naysayers and the perpetrators
I saw the cons and the suckers,
and all them unappreciative muther%$#^^s
The kind of people that break you down to your very core
You know . . . the ungrateful ones that you do the most for

I witnessed Judas's betrayal and Peter's denial
I also saw Benedict Arnold's high treason
There were so many stuck in eternal despair
and those who did evil for no reason

After I took that long, long look
Every inch of my foundation was instantly shook
My soul was so close to being took
I had to free myself from the devil's hook

The devil then asked in a vengeful voice,
"What have you decided, Sherrie, to be your course?
Come down *my* road and be chauffeured in a Rolls Royce."
I felt pushed into a corner, like a Hobson's choice.

I replied,
"Ms. Devil, I just don't want to be that hateful and mean.
God forbid I turn out to be any of those things."
I know when I said God's name, it made that she-devil sting.
As I tried to free myself, I heard some heavenly strings.

I look around, and guess who I see?
It was Robert Johnson, and he was playing for me
Strumming his guitar so beautifully
He came to save my soul and to set me free

Now,
Mr. Johnson was traveling opposite of the she-devil's road.
So I asked, "Mr. Johnson,
I thought at the crossroads you sold your soul?"
He said, "I couldn't stand that heat, baby. I prefer the cold.
Come away with me from this she-devil's stronghold.
I'll tell you all about the day me and my guitar was at the crossroads."

Mr. Johnson confided,
"I know you have been sitting with this devil for a while."
"What took you so long to come and get me?" I asked.
He replied, "I traveled a country mile.
I was sent here from the Motherland,
by way of the African Nile."

I said, "You could have just left me here."
He replied, "Naw, baby, that ain't my style.
See, you are not just anybody—you are my brother's child."
I took his hand immediately, and I began to smile.

As we started to walk, I saw a breathtaking light.
I felt an overwhelming joy as he held my hand tight.
It was so snug and warm that I could not put up a fight.
Something inside just told me, we were traveling right.

And as Mr. Johnson spoke,
I listened to every word he said.
He chuckled and confessed,
"I didn't let that she-devil get into my head.
Even though she caught me at a time
when I had no water, no bread
and feeling so low with the blues sometimes,
even wishing I was dead.
I made up my mind those bad feelings I finally had to shed.
I was sick and tired of being sick and tired,
and was ready to move ahead."

Mr. Johnson then began the story of what happened to him at the crossroads that day.
He simply said, "An angel appeared, Sherrie,
and the devil went away.
Then the angel led me this very same way."

Oooh, I couldn't wait to hear what else Mr. Johnson had to say!
So I eagerly asked, "What happened next?"

Without hesitation, Mr. Johnson replied,
"The angel gave me a pair of brand new shoes
to try on for size.
And walking this road for a while,
out of the ashes, I saw a Phoenix rise.
Just like that light up yonder, you in for a big surprise."

He continued to say,
"An epiphany came to me that day,
and two things I had to realize,
My soul was never for sale, Sherrie,
because it's a priceless prize,
And that was not the devil at the crossroads . . .
it was an angel in disguise."

Mr. Johnson taught me so much that day.
Some lessons I have yet to understand.
But if you ever see me at your crossroads,
*Just smile and take my hand . . .*

# Part 2
# After the Crossroads

*Tropical Storm Faye, Tallahassee, Florida*
*Photo by Sherrie J. Barnes*

"I walked away from all stress and strife
Just got tired of that in my life
Stopped caring who was at fault
No looking back . . . I might turn into salt."
**Sherrie J. Barnes**


"The world is a severe schoolmaster, for its frowns are less
dangerous than its smiles and flatteries and it is a difficult
task to keep in the path of wisdom."
**Phyllis Wheatley, Poet**

# Chapter 7
# Motivation and Inspiration

*"I wish an end to world hunger, and for peace on earth too.
I still wish for more wishes, because a few wishes just
won't do!"*
**Sherrie J. Barnes**

# The Road to the Promised Land

The road to the Promised Land is conducive for ambush
Martin said on that fateful night in April 1968
Meandering paths and tortuous trails
Clear and present dangers all along the way

Attacked by disappointment and betrayal
Early in my travel
Stalled in a quicksand of self-denial
The trip began to unravel

Encountered a militia of naysayers
All ganged up on bandwagons
Gwenivere would have been so proud
Of how I slayed those fire-breathing dragons

Ran into the perilous times
Like Dorothy on the yellow road of brick
But I did not get to go home
On my third heel click

No pain, no gain; no struggle, no progress
Forced to internalize both notions
Because the road became a complete mess
Flooded with strife and commotion

Got blocked by potholes of confusion
My journey came to a complete halt
Had traveled too far to turn back
"Cowgirled up" for the next assault

Besieged by the death of many loved ones
That I still deeply mourn
I prayed for serenity, I prayed for calm
Like the kind before the storm

Just as I covered the pothole
The road divided in two
I pondered at the fork a while
Contemplating what to do

When I let go of bitterness and childish ways
And chose the less-traveled lane
When I traded fear for faith, and love replaced hate
It was then a woman I became

Talents began to blossom
As I saw myself through God's eyes
Vision became universe far
Sight focused on the prize

Dissected the enemy's chest
The way David captured Zion
For the weary there is no rest
Grew the heart of a jungle lion

Unbreakable and invincible
A formidable combination
Is what I transformed into
When I reached my destination

Upon my long awaited arrival
A physical place I did not find
Uncovered a profound revelation
The Promised Land is purely a state of mind

# My Competitor's Creed

Have the perseverance
To stay eternally in the fray
'Cause when big trees fall
Ain't long before day

Don't know what I mean?
Then please continue to read
Follow the lesson carefully
As I take the lead

Fight like a soldier on the field
Unlearn the definition of relax
Take no prisoners in battle
Kill a mosquito with an ax

No guts means no glory
Shed blood, sweat, and tears
Have no uses for excuses
Never succumb to fears

Always reach for higher ground
In practice be devout
Don't just beat your opponent
In his heart, leave no doubt.

"Let's see," said the blind man
As he picked up his hammer and saw
Never get caught off guard
And unveil a fatal flaw

Master your craft like a guru
Your greatest weapon is a cool head
The early bird catches the worm
So be the first out of bed

Engrave deeply in your mind
There's nothing you can't handle
Burn the midnight oil
at both ends of the candle

Surpass expectations
And your name they will forever remember
Never say die
Never ever surrender.

# My Three Wishes

If I had three wishes
I would never ever wash dishes
I'd get a whole lot of kisses
and I'd wish for more wishes

I'd wish my family and friends
To savor a healthy, happy life
I'd wish them the best of everything
Prosperity in their own right

I'd wish an end to world hunger
and for peace on earth too
I'd still wish for more wishes
Because a few wishes just won't do

I'd wish for clean water in Africa
and that *our* story was finally told
I'd wish an end to crimes against humanity
and no warming over the globe

Still not washing dishes, because I wish for more wishes
Like wisdom, faith, and love
I'd wish the homeless a warm bed at night
I'd wish for many blessings from above

I'd wish George Carver was still around
Booker T. Washington close in tow
I'm so glad I wished for more wishes
'Cause there are so many I wish to know

My ancestors, especially my grandmommas
Easily top the list
Of the folks I'd still want around
If I had more wishes to wish

I'd wish everyone common sense
Like when to come in out of the cold
I'd wish enough compassion to forgive and forget
Enough knowing when to hold, and when to fold

Out of all of my wishes, none of them are listless
All are solemn and true
A brave heart, an open mind, and a warm soul
Yes, those are my three wishes for you

# Chapter 8
# Getting My Groove Back

*Bluest Water and White Sands, Nassau, Bahamas*
*Photo by: Sherrie J. Barnes*

*"What would I do? Alone on an island with you. I will follow your cue. Play cat and let you pursue."*

# My Kinda Man

My kinda man
Tucks his shirts in his pants
A real Nat Turner when it's time to take a stance
He and I together, he desires to enhance
So he spoils me all the time with chivalry and romance
Serenades me ever so sweetly whenever we dance
Would not mess up this good thing, given the chance

In his presence, I blossom like a flower
Yes, he possesses that kind of power
My superhero, no jellyback, no coward
My doctor, "on call" at any hour

He keeps me at a sexual peak,
Doesn't know the definition of weak
Pursuit of my pleasure is what he seeks
He will inherit the earth just like the meek

For only me will he be a fool
Understands the karma of the golden rule
Teaches me subjects I never learned in school
Swag like Morris Day and The Time kinda of cool

He appreciates my style and beauty
Lets me con him with my big booty
Leaves me alone when I am moody
For the less fortunate, will go beyond the call of duty

He is my sweet sensation
Seduces me with his conversation
Realizes that the journey is the destination
So after we make love, he gets a *standing* ovation

My kinda man will always have my back
Studies his history, is proud to be Black
Mastered many trades, no regular jack
Situated, sophisticated, will take up my slack
My kinda man . . . a real class act.

# Stranded

What would I do?
Alone on an island with you
I would follow your cue
play cat and let you pursue

You be the he, I be the she
Stay next to me, protect me, and love me for me
In a blue lagoon with you is where I want to be
Sipping coconut milk under a breezy palm tree

Our emotions fill the open air
like incense in a closed space
In each other's presence
We are truly graced

We would build a cozy house
with passion, leaves, and sticks
I would trust that any problem
you could surely fix

Wouldn't it be nice?
To make our own paradise?
Feast on fish, fruit, and rice
Drinking libations to entice

Take morning walks and midnight strolls
To see what our new life unfolds
Your hand I would always hold
Especially when the days grow cold

We would talk for hours and hours
Attain magical powers
Some days may be sour
But you'd still kiss me and bring me flowers

All day we'd frolic in the sea
On this island we'd feel free
Baby just you and me
Sweet love and tranquility

# A Blues for Him

(Ode to Love Jones, Nina, and Darius Lovehall)

*Hey baby, may I blow your mind?*
*Hold on—let me say that again . . . and put it on rewind*
*Hey baby, may I blow your mind?*
*And take you to place where there is no keeping of time*

*First destination, our minds touch*
*An explosion like the latest fashion trend*
*Forget about being "just friends"*
*Let's break each other's hearts*
*Then quickly put them on the mend*

*Second destination, the boondocks of the Milky Way*
*Where our love is a constant rebirth*
*You be my Supernova, and I will be your Nebula*
*We'll have a child, and call her the Universe*

*Hey baby, am I blowing your mind?*
*See, 'cause when I get this blues for HIM, it feels so good*
*I like to keep it on rewind*
*And make this feeling last, like a vintage wine*
*A serenade of Luther and Cheryl . . .*
*If this world were mine, I would place at your feet all that I own, you been*
*so good to me . . .*
*If this world were mine*

What makes our union so sweet?
It's that we earn each other's keep
When we are in the mist of pain
We just jump on Confunkshun's Love Train
Then you send for me like Atlantic Starr,
and we make it a night to remember like Shalimar
Then we kiss, and it feels like kisses of 10,000 angels from above
Then, like Aretha, I give you something you can feel
Fire and desire that ignites Lakeside's kind of real love

Then we give each other injections of our imperfections
and through those defections,
we make a perfect connection

Hey baby, have I blown your mind?
When I get a blues for HIM, it feels so good
I like to keep it on rewind, and make this feeling last,
like a vintage wine
like a serenade of Luther and Cheryl's
If this world were mine, I would place at your feet all that I own, you been
so good to me . . .
if this world were mine
Yeah, I like to keep that on rewind, and make this feeling laaaaast
like a vintage wine.

# Chapter 9
# Just Showing Off

*"Talents began to blossom*
*Saw myself through God's Eyes*
*Vision became universe far*
*Sight focused on the prize."*
**Sherrie J. Barnes**

# My Evolution Will Be *Televised*

My evolution will be *televised*
My swagger will continue to mesmerize
Down on my grind I came to realize
Success delayed is not success denied

See, perseverance is an unrelenting force
'Cause the race is not always to the swift but the one who stays the course
So I mustered up the strength to stay in the fray
Took one for the Gipper and did eight the hard way

Conquered the honor of falling on the sword
At the crossroads with the devil, I chose to stay aboveboard
Shifted into fifth gear and back on one accord
That cute orange dress I can now afford

I walked away from all stress and strife
Just got tired of that in my life
Stopped caring who was at fault
No looking back—I might turn into salt

I haven't changed, I have grown
I don't just apologize, I atone
I appreciate the solace of time alone
Being true to myself—that skill is now honed

Into a Superwoman
From being a Supergirl
Went from a rare diamond
To the eighth wonder of the world
Beautiful with my hair straight
Or with lots and lots of curls
One of many feathers in my cap
My nine sacred pearls

Feel my words deep down inside
Let my eyes be your eyes
Not only an invitation, this is a guide
Into an unveiled soul with no disguise
Like the Phoenix, out of the ashes I rise
This is my evolution
And it will be *televised*

#theGOAT
#LibraWoman
#EmpressEnergy
#DivineTiming

# With a Stroke of My Pen

With a stroke of my pen
I can lead a horse to water *and* make him drink
I can inspire a non-thinker to start to think
I can fill in all the missing links
'Cause when I author a joint, it can never ever stink

With the stroke of my pen
I can place you under my hex
Teach the difference between making love and having sex
Give you the courage to face whatever life has next
Or I can just blow your mind and simply leave you perplexed

With the stroke of my pen
I can determine your fate
I can make a thief give when he wants to take
Make a vegetarian eat steak and a mime elaborate
I can unload all that stress piled up on your plate

With the stroke of my pen
I can make the sun set or rise
I can rotate a hurricane counterclockwise
I can give you an alibi and make you believe lies
Like a red light is blue, and one plus two equals five.

With the stroke of my pen
I can make your dreams a manifestation
I can make the CIA divulge a classified location
I can simplify complex situations
Make the KKK give me a standing ovation
Or I can set you free, like Lincoln's emancipation

With the stroke of my pen
I can make a grown man cry
I can make that grown man cry without a tear
Dropping from that grown man's eye

With the stroke of my pen
I can give your insides a colon cleanse
Take you to a parallel galaxy you've never been
Give you the power of Executive Order 110
Umph, umph, umph, when I stroke with this pen
I can make a churchgoer commit sin
What else can I do, you ask?
I can rewrite the Book of Revelations to come to *my* end

With the stroke of my pen,
and the words you hear me speak,
I can make kings and queens bow down at my feet
I can make a soldier retreat and a DJ miss a beat
I can coerce an Olympic champion to concede defeat

Now I can go on and on
telling you what I do with the stroke of my pen
But unfortunately this lyrical odyssey
has to come to an end.

There is a parable that goes:
if you give a man a fish,
you feed him for a day.
*Teach* a man to fish, and you feed him always

So with a stroke of my pen,
I feed you food for thought with my rhymes
Not *give* you, but *teach* you,
so I can feed you for a lifetime
With the wisdom I've attained as I write deep down from my soul
About all the truisms of life my ancestors told

And when I teach, it will be as the *master* taught,
because that is what created my poetic mold
With a stroke of my pen, **I got the Midas touch** . . .
**what I write turns to gold**.

Made in the USA
Columbia, SC
25 September 2024

42958406R00065